A Grows

by Emmett King

Harcourt
SCHOOL PUBLISHERS

Printed in the United States of America

ISBN 10: 0-15-350616-4
ISBN 13: 978-0-15-350616-1

Ordering Options
ISBN 10: 0-15-350598-2 (Grade 1 On-Level Collection)
ISBN 13: 978-0-15-350598-0 (Grade 1 On-Level Collection)
ISBN 10: 0-15-357771-1 (package of 5)
ISBN 13: 978-0-15-357771-0 (package of 5)

2 3 4 5 6 7 8 9 10   179   15 14 13 12 11 10 09 08 07

I am a little kitten. I am soft. I can smell, but I cannot see yet.

My home is in a box. I need to drink milk to grow.

Look how much I grew.
Now I can see.

I lap up my water. I eat as much food as I can.

I like to play with my
friends. We watch the ducks
fly in the air. We watch the
dogs and the hens.

I like to sit in the sun.

Now the rain falls. It's time
to go back to my box!